COLORING FISH

OVER 40 EXTRAORDINARY
PICTURES WITH FULL
COLORING GUIDES

ARCTURUS

ARCTURUS

ISBN 978-1-78599-206-3
AD004981US

Manufactured in China

2 4 6 8 10 9 7 5 3 1

Introduction

The fish of the world come in numerous and gorgeous forms, many of which are unfamiliar to us except in tropical aquaria and on our television screens–but we do have the chance to see them there. It is hard to imagine the impact that some of the more exotic species shown in these pages would have had on the majority of nineteenth-century readers, who would mainly have known only the gray and brown fish harvested from rivers and coastal waters. The illustrations here come from *The Naturalist's Library*, which was edited by the great Scottish naturalist Sir William Jardine (1800-1874) and issued in a set of 40 volumes with more than 1,300 plates engraved by his brother-in-law, William Lizars (1788-1859).

There's endless interest to be had in depicting the colors and textures of a fish's body, but it's very hard to do this from life. Working from these illustrations, you will be able to study them in detail and follow Lizars' exquisite work. And, too, you can simply revel in the pleasure of coloring in, which is now hugely popular with adults for the relaxation and satisfaction in one's skills it brings.

The choice of art materials now goes far beyond the crayons you may have used when you were a child; you can also buy oil-based, wax-based or watersoluble color pencils, colorfast and exhibition quality. You can use them dry, blending them with your finger or a paper stump, or dilute them with oil, or water for the watersoluble pencils. Alternatively, you can paint your fish–a small watercolor set and a medium-sized round brush is all you need. Whichever you choose, you'll find many hours of enjoyment from trying to match the skills of William Lizars.

Diana Vowles

Key: *List of plates*

1 *Centropristes nigricanus*
(American Black Bass)

2 *Etelis carbunculus*
(Ruby-colored Etelis)

3 *Apogon trimaculatus*
(Mediterranean Apogon)

4 *Cheilodipterus arabicus*
(Arabian Cheilodipterus)

5 *Genus perca* (Common Perch)

6 *Diploprion bifaclatum*
(Two-banded Diploprion)

7 *Mesoprion uninotatus*
(One-spotted Mesoprion)

8 *Chalceus macrolepitdotus*
(Pink-tailed Chalceus)

9 *Serranus scriba* (Lettered Serranus)

10 *Centrarchus cyanopterus*
(Blue-finned Centrarchus)

11 *Dactylopterus orientalis*
(Oriental Dactylopterus)

12 *Serrasalmo niger* (Red-eyed Piranha)

13 *Exocetus volitans*
(Common Flying Fish)

14 *Centrarchus cychla*
(Cychla-like Centrarchus)

15 *Zanclus cornutus*
(Horned Zanclus or Chaetodon)

16 *Argus pteraclis* (Pteraclis Ocellatus)

17 *Lethrynus esculentus*
(Edible Lethrynus)

18 *Prionace glauca* (Blue Shark)

19 *Serranus anthias* (Spined Serranus)

20 *Monocentris cornutus*
(Armed Monocentris)

21 *Peristedion cataphractum*
(Mailed Peristedion)

22 *Ostracion cubicus*
(Spotted Ostracion)

23 *Acantharus hepatus*
(Yellow-bellied Acanthurus)

24 *Zeus faber* (John Dory)

25 *Trachinus radiatus*
(Radiated Weaver)

26 *Serranus altivelis*
(Large-finned Serranus)

27 *Annarrhicus lupus* (Wolf Fish)

28 *Labrus mixtus* (Blue-striped Wrasse)

29 *Chimaera monstrosa*
(Northern Chimaera)

30 *Labrus formosus* (Painted Labrus)

31 *Cychla rubro-ocellata*
(Red-spotted Cycla)

32 *Echinorhinus spinosus*
(Spinous Shark)

33 *Huro nigricanus*
(The Black Bass of the Huron)

34 *Mesoprion chrysurus*
(Golden-tailed Mesoprion)

35 *Acestra aequorea* (Equorcal Pipe
Fish) *and Hippocampus brevirostris*
(Short-nosed Seahorse)

36 *Peristedion malarmat*
(Mailed Gurnard)

37 *Acerina vulgaris* (The Ruffe)

38 *Doras castaneo-ventris*
(Brown Dorsal-striped Doras)

39 *Serrasalmo punctatus*
(Spotted Saw-bellied Salmon)

40 *Sudis gigas* (Gigantic Sudis)

41 *Gasterosteus spinosa*
(Fifteen-spined Stickleback nest and
eggs)

42 *Pomatomus telescopium*
(The Large-eyed Pomatome)

43 *Serrasalmo piranha*
(Piranha Saw-bellied Salmon)

44 *Pimelodus insignis*
(Black-spotted Green Pimelodus)

Centropristes nigricanus

American Black Bass

Etelis carbunculus

Ruby-colored Etelis

Apogon trimaculatus

Mediterranean Apogon

Cheilodipterus arabicus

Arabian Cheilodipterus

Genus perca

Common Perch

Diploprion bifaclatum

Two-banded Diploprion

Mesoprion uninotatus

One-spotted Mesoprion

Chalceus macrolepidotus

Pink-tailed Chalceus

Serranus scriba

Lettered Serranus

Centrarchus cyanopterus

Blue-finned Centrarchus

Dactylopterus orientalis

Oriental Dactylopterus

Serrasalmo niger

Red-eyed Piranha

Exocetus volitans

Common Flying Fish

Centrarchus cychla

Cychla-like Centrarchus

Zanclus cornutus

Horned Zanclus or Chaetodon

Argus pteraclis

Pteraclis Ocellatus

Lethrynus esculentus

Edible Lethrynus

Prionace glauca

Spined Serranus

Monocentris cornutus

Armed Monocentris

Mailed Peristedion

Ostracion cubicus

Spotted Ostracion

Acantharus hepatus

Yellow-bellied Acanthurus

Zeus faber

John Dory

Trachinus radiatus

Radiated Weaver

Serranus altivelis

Large-finned Serranus

Annarrhicus lupus

Wolf Fish

Labrus mixtus

Blue-striped Wrasse

Chimaera monstrosa

Northern Chimaera

Labrus formosus

Painted Labrus

Cychla rubro-ocellata

Red-spotted Cycla

Echinorhinus spinosus

Spinous Shark

Huro nigricanus

The Black Bass of the Huron

Mesoprion chrysurus

Golden-tailed Mesoprion

Equorcal Pipe Fish and Short-nosed Seahorse

Peristedion malarmat

Mailed Gurnard

Acerina vulgaris

The Ruffe

38

Doras castaneo–ventris

Brown Dorsal-striped Doras

Serrasalmo punctatus

Gigantic Sudis

Gasterosteus spinosa

Fifteen-spined Stickleback nest and eggs

Pomatomus telescopium

The Large-eyed Pomatome

Serrasalmo piranha

Piranha Saw-bellied Salmon

Pimelodus insignis

Black-spotted Green Pimelodus